Scotland's Black Diamonds

Coal Mining in Scotland

Guthrie Hutton

Published by Stenlake Publishing in association with the
Scottish Mining Museum, Lady Victoria Colliery, Newtongrange.

SCOTLAND'S
BLACK DIAMONDS
SCOTTISH MINING MUSEUM

SCOTLAND'S
BLACK DIAMONDS
SCOTTISH MINING MUSEUM

Fife
Clackmannan
Stirling
Lothian
Lanark / Central
Ayr
Douglas
Machrihanish
Sanquhar
Girvan Valley
Canonbie

Scotland's coalfields

the
from dead trees to black diamonds

The trees that formed coal were not as we know them today, they were like giant ferns. They flourished in swamps beside great river deltas, with new growth constantly replacing old. When the river changed course, or when the ground sank, the sea moved in and covered the rotting trees with mud and sand. Upheaval or a buildup of silt allowed the forest to grow again, starting the cycle of growth, decay, silt cover and re-growth again. This process was repeated many times and as each layer of rotting vegetation was compressed under further tons of mud and sand it was gradually turned by time, pressure and heat into coal. The mud and sand solidified into various types of rock. In the geological periods that followed, massive earth movements bent, buckled and broke the flat beds of coal, molten volcanic rock flowed around them and the land masses that formed Scotland buried them. For millions of years wind, rain and then ice wore away the covering rocks, until they became so eroded that the coal came close to the surface again.

The geological era when most coal was formed is known as the Carboniferous period. It lasted about 60 million years and ended around 200 million years ago, when dinosaurs were beginning to appear. They died out 65 million years ago and man evolved 2 million years ago. Scots are known to have been burning coal for about a thousand years.

Fossil Grove at Victoria Park, Glasgow—fossils of primitive plant and animal life are often found in coal or coal-bearing strata

story of coal

So great was the value of coal to the development of industrial Britain that the output of the nation's mines came to be known as 'black diamonds'.

Comparing a lump of coal to a gem like a diamond may seem perverse, but the two substances have one thing in common; both are forms of the chemical element carbon. Diamonds, created by volcanic action, are the purest carbon, but coal's carbon content varies. There are many types of coal too, all the fossilised remains of trees and other vegetation that lived and died millions of years ago.

different types of coal formed

Anthracite—Shiny, hard, brittle and clean, was formed in different ways; Scottish anthracite is coal that was altered by heat from volcanic rock, or by earth movements. It has a very high carbon content and burns with great heat, no smoke and little flame.

Bituminous Coals—Bright and glossy or a dull black, they are easy to light and burn with a bright flame, but can be smoky. They are best for household use, steel-making and gas generation. **Sub-bituminous [or Steam] Coals** were used in boilers, locomotives and ships.

Parrot or Cannel Coal—Hard, compact and rich in gas, was formed by small plant material rotting in shallow lakes. It is called 'cannel' [candle] coal because it burns with a bright flame and 'parrot' because of the crackling sound it makes when burning. Some cannel coals can be carved, polished and made into jewellery or models—furniture was even made from cannel coal in the nineteenth century.

Peat—Cut and used as fuel in parts of Scotland, it is not coal, but compacted vegetable matter which has broken down in water and become partly carbonised. If buried and subjected to enormous pressure for millions of years it would turn into coal.

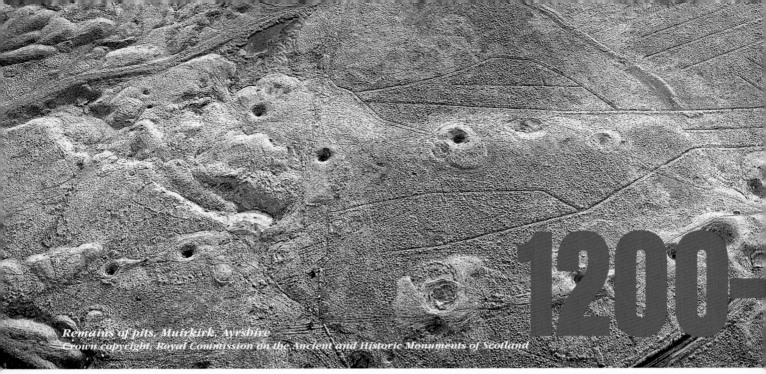

Remains of pits, Muirkirk, Ayrshire
Crown copyright, Royal Commission on the Ancient and Historic Monuments of Scotland

1200-

Miner working below roof propped with 'trees'

Bell pit

Known to have been worked by monks at abbeys like Newbattle and Dunfermline in the thirteenth century, coal was almost certainly used before that. The earliest workings were shallow quarries where coal was exposed in river valleys, or broke the surface of the ground—out-cropped. To get to deeper coal, shallow pits, not much more than a hole in the ground, were sunk. They were undercut at the bottom into the shape of a bell and worked to the limit of safety. Other pits were then sunk alongside, pock-marking an area. As techniques developed, these 'bell' pits were extended with tunnels radiating from the base.

4

Old stoop and room limestone workings.

-1750

Overcome by gas

Intermediate platforms and ladders were used in deeper shafts, to gain access to the pit and carry coal to the surface. Windlasses and horse gins were developed and people rode up and down sitting in a rope sling or on a stick. Baskets and barrels were the forerunners of the 'cages' of later years. Swinging freely on the end of a rope, if they became snagged, they could tip out their occupants or contents.

Miners started leaving pillars of coal, known as stoops, to support the roof. The extracted areas were called rooms. 'Stoop and room' mines could be unstable if too much coal was taken and too little support left for the roof, so larger stoops were left. The miners could then work to the mine's limit and retreat to the entrance removing the stoops and letting the roof collapse behind them. They could also leave stoops in place to support buildings on the surface. Propping of roof and walls developed so that workings could go deeper. Early miners used what was to hand, a practical necessity reflected by later miners who called timber props 'trees'.

Coal was taken out in large lumps, known as 'big coal', or 'great coal'. These fetched high prices, because people could see what they were getting from a trade that was not known for honesty! The smaller lumps were called 'chews', or 'wee coal', and the unsaleable dross, 'panwood' or 'limecoal', used to fire salt pans or lime kilns.

To get the large lumps the miner first 'holed' [undercut], the coal for about three feet with a short-shafted pick and supported the overhang with 'sprags' [short props]. He then broke the coal down in lumps with wedges driven into the coal face, or a crow bar.

hazards

The early miner's greatest hazard came from falling earth or rock—still the greatest danger. Collapsing shafts or roofs could also block passages and trap miners, exposing them to a buildup of gas.

Early mines relied on natural ventilation. As workings went deeper without proper ventilation, problems grew and gases began to take their toll. Men had their lives blighted or shortened by the foul atmosphere and some were poisoned where they worked. The more dramatic fires and explosions began to occur in deep pits, with extensive workings.

Water was both a nuisance and a danger. Bucket chains, driven by a horse or windlass, raised water from pits, but in some areas drainage mines, known as levels or adits, were driven from coal seams to river valleys. Notable Scottish examples include the two and three-quarter mile long Holmsyke level at Wilsontown in Lanarkshire, the Fordell Day Level in Fife and the Mavisbank Day Level at Loanhead.

the moat pit

The Moat Pit at Culross was developed by Sir George Bruce of Carnock in 1590 and was a remarkable example of mining innovation. It had two shafts, one on the land and one which came to the surface on an artificial island below the high tide line. Boats could come alongside and load coal directly from the pit. Sea water constantly leaked into the workings. They were drained by a large windlass-like mechanism known as a gin. Worked by horses walking in a circle, it lifted the water in thirty-six buckets attached to a chain. The buckets were emptied into a trough which led to the sea. Alas, the pit was overwhelmed and flooded in March 1625 when a very high tide coincided with a violent storm in the Forth.

early industries

Making iron

People needed fuel to heat their homes and food, or to make things. Fire had been used to make pottery, iron and glass since prehistoric times and these began to develop on an industrial scale with the use of coal. Industries like sugar boiling, soap making, brewing and distilling developed and, after about 1760, large amounts of lime mortar were being made in huge kilns to meet the demand created by extensive building in Scotland's towns and cities.

Making iron cannon balls

salt pans

*Salt pans and mine buildings on
Preston Island in the Firth of Forth*

Salt was vital for the preservation of food. Its manufacture, by boiling sea water in large pans, became a major Scottish industry, helped by the proximity of coal to the sea. Salt was the country's third largest export in the seventeenth century. The main concentrations of salt pans in Scotland were around the Firth of Forth and Ayrshire. Some place names like Grangepans, Prestonpans and Saltcoats reflect salt-making origins. At Brora in Sutherland a small pocket of poor quality 'Jurassic' coal, formed about 160 million years ago, was used in salt extraction and brick-making.

Pan houses were usually stone sheds, with a chimney or slot in the roof to let out the smoke and steam. They were often clustered together in groups close to the sea shore above high water mark. Typical pans were rectangular, about eighteen feet by nine, eighteen inches deep and made of cast iron. They were raised off the floor, on stone or brick pillars, and were fired evenly underneath. Reservoirs were built close to the high water mark with entry channels to keep them as free of seaborne debris as possible. They were known as bucket pots, because buckets were used to fill early pans, but later the water was pumped to the pans from the pots.

When the water in the pan was nearly boiling the salter threw bullock's blood into it to bring impurities to the surface. These were skimmed off leaving a clear liquid and this process was repeated until the evaporation was complete and the salt drawn off. The process required sixteen tons of coal to produce one ton of salt.

Excise tax changes in 1823 made imported salt cheaper and effectively killed the evaporation industry.

Salt pan house

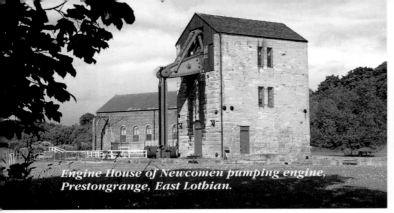

Engine House of Newcomen pumping engine, Prestongrange, East Lothian.

House at Bo'ness where James Watt experimented with steam engines.

the machine

Thomas Newcomen & James Watt

The most complete and powerful engine of any that the philosophy of and genius of men have presented to the world.

Robert Bald, mining engineer (1812)

The scale of mining in the early eighteenth century was limited by the amount of water that could be drained from a pit, or the weight of coal that could be lifted. This changed when Thomas Newcomen developed a working steam engine. Newcomen was a craftsman and inventor from Devon whose engine revolutionised British industry, although he neither sought nor received credit from the scientific establishment of the day.

Newcomen's engine was known as a condensing or atmospheric engine, because a jet of water was used to condense steam in the cylinder and create a vacuum. Atmospheric pressure then pushed the piston into the vacuum. Newcomen engines, used at mines for pumping, were known as 'fire' engines, because they burned coal to turn water into steam. The first went into commercial use at a Staffordshire mine in 1712. Two were set up in Scotland around 1719 and others followed, but not many because they were expensive.

By 1757 Glasgow University had a model of a Newcomen steam engine but it did not work well and a young instrument maker, James Watt, was asked to find out why. He quickly concluded that Newcomen's system wasted steam and developed a theory that the engine's performance and fuel economy would be improved if the steam could escape into a separate condenser, instead of being lost.

James Watt

Watt's ideas attracted John Roebuck, one of the founders of the great Carron ironworks. Roebuck also owned mines in the Bo'ness area, but flooding had brought them to the brink of failure. In 1769, he invited Watt to build a steam engine for mine drainage, but the water beat them and Roebuck's mining business collapsed. Watt headed for Birmingham where he teamed up with entrepreneur, Matthew Boulton. There he improved the economy and efficiency of steam engines, and adapted them to provide rotational drive; to such effect that Boulton and Watt became the principal suppliers of steam engines in Britain.

Iron foundry at Taynuilt, Argyll

age 1750–1850

iron & the Carron Company

The small-scale charcoal-burning Scottish iron industry was eclipsed when the first blast furnace of the huge Carron ironworks started production on Boxing Day 1760. It burned coke—the solid material left after the gases have been extracted from coal. The company was set up by two Birmingham businessmen, John Roebuck and Samuel Garbett, and William Cadell from East Lothian. They set out to establish a large ironworks in Scotland and selected a site near the mouth of the River Carron which gave them water power to drive the works, access to the sea for transport and proximity to rich mineral reserves at Bo'ness. The works made a variety of products, including the Carronade, a devastating, large bore, short barrelled, naval cannon.

Carronade

Falkirk Museums; Callendar House

Muirkirk ironworks, Ayrshire

The sheer scale of the Carron operation inhibited competition until 1779 when Wilsontown ironworks was set up. Others followed: Clyde (1786), Omoa (1787) and Shotts (1802) in Lanarkshire; Glenbuck (1785) and Muirkirk (1787) in Ayrshire and Balgonie (1802) in Fife.

9

Coal wagons
shipped on the Forth & Clyde Canal

The Carron River was also where work on the Forth and Clyde Canal began in 1768. At the time roads were poor and the principal form of freight transport was coastal shipping, which the canal extended by linking the east and west coasts. The canal helped Glasgow to expand and the city's development was also enhanced by cheap coal brought in by the Monkland Canal. This canal was completed in 1793 and quite by chance was in the right place to serve the iron industry of Coatbridge when it developed in the 1830s.

canals

Horse-drawn railways, moving coal from mines to ports, were working in Scotland before the canals were developed. The first was the Tranent Wagonway, laid down in 1722 to link the Tranent pits to the harbour and salt pans at Cockenzie. The Fordell Railway in Fife was laid about 1760 to take coal from the Fordell Estate collieries to the new harbour of St David's on the Firth of Forth. Another railway was laid from the Sauchie pits to Alloa Harbour in 1768. A steam locomotive was tried in 1819 on the Duke of Portland's Kilmarnock to Troon railway, but it damaged the rails and the line reverted to horse haulage.

The Monkland and Kirkintilloch Railway was opened in 1826 and, in 1831, became the first locomotive-hauled public railway in Scotland. It brought coal from the Coatbridge area to the Forth & Clyde Canal for onward shipping to Edinburgh through the Union Canal. This canal brought competition to the city's coal suppliers, and the price of coal dropped when it was completed in 1822.

Other railways started to spread across Lanarkshire to serve the growing coal and iron industries, the most significant being the Glasgow and Garnkirk Railway. It opened in 1831 from Coatbridge to Port Dundas in Glasgow and although its novelty value made it popular with passengers, its real purpose was to move coal. The railway age, and with it, industrial expansion, had begun.

Garnkirk and Glasgow Railway

The mining industry responded to these developments. More efficient pumps controlled water levels, allowing shafts to be sunk deeper and workings to be extended further underground. Steam engines were adapted to replace the old windlasses and horse gins, and the wooden tubs or baskets used in shafts were replaced by 'cages'. Despite the name these were little more than platforms which gave no protection to the men. Hemp ropes too were replaced by stronger, wire ropes.

and railways
mining developments

Underground haulage by women and children was the last link, from coal face to market, to be mechanised. Roads could be low, narrow, steep, wet and soft underfoot, but women carried huge loads along them in basketwork creels. Children wearing a harness over their shoulders dragged carts or iron-shod, sledge-like, boxes known as 'slypes'. In some conditions they crawled on all fours. Commercial pressures, and legislation banning women and children working underground, caused roadways to be enlarged. Ponies began to be used in increasing numbers. They hauled 'rakes' [trains] of 'hutches' [small boxlike carts] on narrow rails. Steam haulages, working through a system of cables and pulleys, were also developed. The engines were sited either underground or on the surface, with cables going down the shaft. Haulage cables could be dangerous. Many men were caught and injured by them, and could be killed by hutches running out of control if a cable broke.

Davy lamp

The number of accidents grew with increased mechanisation, but deeper shafts, extended workings and inadequate ventilation, exposed miners to another hazard—explosive gas. The first recorded death in Britain from a gas explosion was in Durham in 1621, but miners continued working with candles or oil lamps until 1813 when Dr Clanny invented the first safe, if impractical, lamp. Two years later George Stevenson and Sir Humphrey Davy both developed lamps, but only Davy's name became associated with them. Scottish miners however stubbornly acknowledge Clanny's part in the story by calling their lamps 'Glenny's'— a local version of his name. Davy lamps enclosed the flame with a wire gauze, a design which became the prototype for the many types of safety lamps that followed.

Modern 'Glennie', flame safety lamp

A shaft at Victoria Colliery, Nitshill

Glasgow Museums and Archives

Sir Humphrey Davy

Ventilating the sometimes extensive warren of passages and caverns was achieved by directing the airflow with barriers. These were made of brattice cloth—canvas, treated for underground conditions and fireproofed—stretched over a wooden frame. Wooden trap-doors allowed access through the barriers. The most common form of ventilation was an underground furnace: the idea of a roaring fire expelling explosive gas may seem odd, but furnaces were not in themselves dangerous. They were sited at the base of a shaft and by expelling hot air up it, like a chimney, they drew fresh air into the pit, down another shaft. What made them hazardous was that the volume of air fluctuated. Methane gas becomes dangerous when mixed with a certain quantity of air, and many men died before the industry understood what was happening.

There was a steady toll through the first half of the nineteenth century, but in 1850 an explosion at Commonhead, Airdrie, killed eighteen men. The furnace had been allowed to go out over a two day holiday, and by starting it up a dangerous quantity of air was added to a build up of gas in a pit where miners used naked flame lamps. It was Scotland's worst mining disaster, until the following year when sixty-one men and boys were killed in an explosion at the Victoria pit, Nitshill, the deepest pit in Scotland. The industry's ability to go down to greater depths had outstripped its understanding of gas and the way it behaved. Victoria pit was regarded as a showpiece of mining engineering and a model of it was due to have been displayed at the Great Exhibition at Crystal Palace, but was never shown.

EXPLOSIONS

mine gases

The process whereby ancient plant life rotted under pressure and turned into coal, also formed gas which remained trapped until miners cut into the coal. The types and quantities of gas varied, as did the dangers. The most obvious risk was from explosions, but the long hours of exposure to a foul and sometimes poisonous atmosphere also sapped miners' health. Improvements in ventilation, often prompted by lessons learned from disasters, became an integral part of mine engineering. As a consequence powerful fans began to be used.

Mine gases have names which all end in 'damp'; which is derived from the German word *dampf*, which means vapour.

Blackdamp [Carbon Dioxide] is a suffocating gas, slightly heavier than air. Miners could tell when it was present because it dimmed a lamp flame.

Firedamp [Methane] is lighter than air and can explode when mixed with air; the most explosive mixture is about one part gas to nine and a half parts air.

Whitedamp [Carbon Monoxide] is a highly poisonous gas present in the cocktail of gases after a fire or explosion. This mixture is also known as **Afterdamp**.

Stinkdamp [Sulphuretted Hydrogen] is a very poisonous gas, with the smell of rotten eggs. It can be inhaled in fatal quantities because it first dulls the senses.

Testing for gas

13

iron and steel

King Coal and the

Cold-blast furnaces, as at Carron, used huge quantities of fuel and were expensive to operate, but in 1828, James Beaumont Neilson developed a process of burning furnace gases to heat air before blasting it into the furnace. It transformed the industry. Neilson's hot-blast furnace could burn Scottish splint coal straight from the mine. Splint coal was hard and when burned in the furnace did not cake into a solid mass, like other coals which had to go through the additional process of being coked—baked in an oven to remove the gases. Production costs were slashed and huge profits made. With ready supplies of blackband ironstone and splint coal, the Coatbridge area became the country's iron capital. In 1830 William Baird—ignoring Neilson's patent—set up the Gartsherrie ironworks with hot-blast furnaces. It was followed by four other works—Summerlee, Calder, Dundyvan and Langloan, which, along with a dozen malleable ironworks, filled Coatbridge with noise, smoke and fire—dark by day and light by night. It was aptly described as 'no worse place out of hell', or 'hell with the lid off'. Other hot-blast furnaces were set up elsewhere, mainly in Lanarkshire and Ayrshire, and at Carron.

Tapping a blast furnace

Making steel rods

1850–1913
Workshop of the World

Processes were developed in the 1860s to make steel on an industrial scale; steel is pure, refined iron with a carefully controlled carbon content. 'Convertors', which burned off the carbon in cast iron, began to be used after Henry Bessemer, the son of an English iron-founder, perfected the process. Scottish steel makers preferred another process called open-hearth in which a shallow bath-like furnace was charged with molten iron, scrap and limestone and swept by the flames of burning gas. Unwanted elements oxidised in the high temperatures and combined with the limestone to form slag which floated on top and was drained off when the furnace was tapped. Although open-hearth was a slow process, it made a high quality steel. These furnaces were sometimes known as Siemens or Siemens/Martin after the men who developed them.

Scotland's big iron companies did not go into steel production and it was left to others to set up steel works. Chemical manufacturer Sir Charles Tennant started the Steel Company of Scotland at Hallside, Cambuslang. Other works were established in Lanarkshire by David Colville & Sons, William Beardmore and the Lanarkshire Steel Company. Merry & Cunninghame's Glengarnock works in Ayrshire made steel as well as iron, but otherwise there was little integration between the industries.

Steel making with open hearth furnaces

Demand for coal grew rapidly through the second half of the nineteenth century and mining expanded in response, but this unfettered production compromised safety. The Victoria pit disaster had remained the worst in Scotland for over twenty years, but on 22 October 1877 a series of violent explosions ripped through Blantyre Nos. 2 and 3 pits. Over 200 men were killed. It remains Scotland's worst mining disaster. The official report put the death-toll at 207, but it may have been higher—no proper check was made of who went down that morning! A spark or naked light was thought to have ignited some gas, but ventilation, and a complicated underground layout, almost certainly contributed too. The pit was ventilated by a large furnace, but the fires may have subsided during the change-over from night to day shifts and caused the air flow to fluctuate. Whatever the cause a ventilating fan of 200,000 cubic feet per minute capacity was installed after the disaster.

DISASTER

This, however, was not the only answer, because in 1887, a similar series of explosions killed seventy-three men at Udston Colliery, Hamilton, even 'though it was already equipped with a large capacity fan. At the enquiry it was shown that the initial gas explosion had raised clouds of coal dust, which had exploded and set off more gas and dust explosions. Udston and Blantyre were both dry, dusty pits and the explosions went on for some time—Blantyre's is said to have lasted for about four minutes—clearly not one, but many blasts. After Udston it became standard practice, required by law, liberally to scatter limestone dust through underground workings to render coal dust inert and stifle explosions.

Ventilation also contributed to Scotland's next worst disaster, at Mauricewood Colliery, Penicuik, in 1889. The fire broke out in an engine house deep underground, but an open ventilation door caused smoke and fumes to circulate back into the pit: sixty-three men and boys died.

As a result of lessons learned from these and other disasters, ventilation became an integral part of pit design and furnaces generally were replaced by fans.

Blantyre Colliery, No 3 shaft

the rising toll

1853   Broken winding rope, Cowdenbeath—5 dead.
1877   Explosion at Blantyre—207 [or more] dead.
1877   Inundation of mud, Larkhall—4 dead.
1878   Explosion at Barwood, Kilsyth—17 dead.
1879   Explosion at Blantyre—25 dead.
1887   Explosion at Udston—73 dead.
1889   Fire at Mauricewood, Penicuik—63 dead.

1895   Explosion at Quarter, Dunipace—13 dead.
1893   Explosion at Herbertshire, Denny—2 dead.
1895   Fire at Kinneddar, Fife—9 dead.
1895   Flood at Auchenharvie, Saltcoats—9 dead.
1897   Flood at Devon, Clackmannanshire— 6 dead.
1901   Inundation of peat at Donibristle, Cowdenbeath—8 dead.

Output from the Scottish coal industry peaked in 1913 and employment stood at 147,500. The worst accident that year was a fire at Cadder near Bishopbriggs which killed twenty-two men, but there were others and half of these were on the surface:

fatalities:	surface :	171	underground :	175
serious accidents:	surface :	800	underground :	695
people disabled for over seven days:	surface :	17,096	underground :	16,368

THE GLASGOW HERALD, MONDAY, MAY 30, 1887

THE SCENE OF THE EXPLOSION.

Udston Colliery after the explosion

Stone dusting at Wellesley Colliery, Fife

Mauricewood Colliery, Penicuik

Congrams—
"Boiler, Glasgow."
ESTABLISHED OVER HALF A CENTURY.

WILLIAM WILSON & CO
LILYBANK BOILER WORKS.
GLASGOW.

Steam Users are invited to call at our New Works, LONDON ROAD, GLASGOW, and inspect the New and Up-to-date Plant installed there for Flanging, Welding, Riveting, etc.

Heat and steam, produced by burning coal, provided industry with its power. Smoking chimney stacks came to dominate towns and cities. People got used to dirt and noise as the country was given over to rapid industrial expansion. Foundries processed metal, which engineering works used to make machines. These in turn were used by other manufacturers to make a vast array of products including ships, chemicals, textiles, jute, linoleum, carpets and ceramics.

industrial growth & the

Niddry Castle oilworks, Winchburgh

Fireclay was extracted from clay or coal mines and baked in ovens to make furnace-bricks, tiles, pipes and sanitary ware. The clay was originally the muddy bed of the swamp, where the coal-trees grew, and lay underneath the coal as a rock-hard mineral. Brickworks or potteries were set up alongside some collieries.

Coal heated people's homes and was also the basis of two new forms of heating and lighting—gas and paraffin oil. William Murdoch experimented in a cave near his home in Lugar, Ayrshire, to extract gas from coal and perfected his ideas while working with Boulton and Watt in Birmingham. Glasgow chemist James Young set up the world's first oil refinery at Bathgate in 1851, to distil oil from cannel coal. From it grew Scotland's shale oil industry which made paraffin, petrol, oils, candles and other chemical products—its founder became known as 'Paraffin Young'.

18

The coal industry had to grow rapidly to keep up with this industrial expansion. Railways opened up new coalfields, new pits were sunk and underground workings extended to new limits. Scottish coal output rose from about three million tons in 1830 to a peak of over forty-two million tons in 1913; about 14 per cent of UK output. But by 1913 the great Lanarkshire industry was losing its dominant position within Scotland.

growing coal industry

LOCOMOTIVES

ANY TYPE.

ASK US FOR SPECIFICATIONS AND PRICES.

HIGHEST SPECIFICATIONS, MATERIALS, AND WORKMANSHIP.

STANDARD 4 WHEELED 16IN. SHUNTING ENGINE.

For IRON and STEELWORKS and COLLIERIES. with Heavy Haulages and Short Curves.

ANDREW BARCLAY, SONS & CO., LTD.,
LOCOMOTIVE ENGINEERS. Caledonia Works, KILMARNOCK.

output:	1900	1913
Lanarkshire	56%	41%
Ayrshire	14%	10%
Fife and Kinross	12%	23%
Stirlingshire	6%	7%
Midlothian	4%	8%
West Lothian	3%	4.5%
Clackmannanshire	1%	1%
Dunbartonshire	1%	1%
East Lothian	1%	2.5%
Argyll and Dumfries	1%	1.5%
Renfrewshire	1%	0.5%

Many of the country's major collieries had become established by 1913, the peak year of production and the industry was supporting a large number of equipment makers. Some firms, like Grant Ritchie of Kilmarnock, made a range of equipment as did Andrew Barclay, also of Kilmarnock, although they specialised in industrial locomotives. Fullerton, Hodgart & Barclay of Paisley, and Murray & Paterson of Coatbridge, made winding engines. Others like the Blantyre Engineering Company built colliery installations, and a host of large and small companies supplied lamps, brattice cloth, explosives, railway wagons, washing plants, rails and hundreds of miles of steel rope.

Supplies of coal went by sea to coastal communities although much of Scotland's coal, particularly from pits in Fife and the Lothians, was exported worldwide. An expanding infrastructure of railways, and docks like Methil, Burntisland, Leith and Bo'ness, were developed to supply these markets. Ayrshire ports were developed to send coal to Ireland and the Western Isles.

Methil Docks

The First World War abruptly ended the years of expansion. Exports were hit as sales of nearly three million tons of Scottish coal to Germany stopped. Enemy warships and mines made the Russian market almost impossible to supply. Lost exports to the coal companies meant lost jobs for the miners, many of whom responded to the call to arms. Belatedly the industry realised that it needed experienced men to produce coal in the national interest, but 25 per cent of the workforce had already left in the first year of the war. The severe labour shortage was compounded by a scarcity of railway trucks, hutches and pit timber. Inadequate coal supplies began to inhibit industrial output. Price controls were introduced, enlistment of underground workers was halted and some men were brought back from military service. From June 1916 mining became a reserved occupation [one which took precedence over military service].

WORLD WAR I

The industry was in a bad way by the end of the war. Production had been pursued at the expense of development and there was no new capacity to replace ageing pits; output was down by 25 per cent and exports by 70 per cent. Wartime price controls, that had kept prices at an artificial level after the war, were suddenly dropped by the Government in 1921. Prices and wages fell immediately and the industry descended into industrial chaos. Old, unprofitable pits closed and manpower fell by about 40 per cent.

There were some hopeful signs. Sinking of the great Polkemmet Colliery, which had been stopped by the war, was completed in the 1920s, but Lanarkshire's decline continued and was only relieved by the development of coking-coal pits at Cardowan, Kingshill and Overtown. While the old heartland of the Scottish coal industry struggled, Fife forged ahead. Two rival companies developed new capacity; the Wemyss Coal Company radically redeveloped their Michael Colliery and the Fife Coal Company began their state of the art Comrie Colliery. By the late 1930s the industry was beginning to recover and the last thing it needed was another war. But alas, that is what it got.

surveyor's dial

HEROES OF THE MINE. (1)

We sing of our soldiers and sailors,
Brave deeds they have done o'er the foam,
But what of our lads who work down the mine,
Little of them may be known?
They start out for work in the morning,
With many a joke and a laugh,
With never a thought of the danger
As they go down the shaft.

WORDS BY PERMISSION OF THE LAWRENCE WRIGHT MUSIC CO.,
29, CONDUIT STREET, LEICESTER.   BAMFORTH COPYRIGHT

WILLS'S CIGARETTES.

MINE SURVEYING.

We won the war...
We can win the coal
The same skill in handling complex weapons and powerful machines that was demonstrated in war will be more and more needed in modern mining.

WORLD WAR II

Use of the high-speed electric drill for boring holes in the face for explosives, calls for a high degree of accuracy.

The pattern of miners leaving the industry to join the services, or to earn more money in munitions factories, was repeated when war broke out. Again the Government reacted slowly to the loss of manpower. Mining was declared a reserved occupation in 1941, conscripts to the forces could volunteer for underground work and men who had left for other industries and the services were brought back. But manpower levels remained stubbornly low and targets were not being met.

Roadways must stand up to heavy pressure. Steel arches are used on permanent roads, and fixing them is an expert's job.

In 1943 the Minister of Labour and National Service, Ernest Bevin, introduced a scheme in which every tenth conscript went into the mines, instead of the forces. Few knew anything about mining, many had already prepared for war by training with cadet corps, but none could do anything about it. They were called Bevin Boys. Some refused to go underground and were sent to prison. They were all A1 fit when they started, but some died and others were injured. They got no uniform, no medals and were only allowed to march in Remembrance Day parades for the first time in 1998.

Mining machinery has a hard life, and requires regular maintenance. Here a skilled mechanic is going over a modern Diesel locomotive.

Machines driven by compressed air were first used in Glasgow in 1853 and, in 1864, William Baird & Co. tried out a compressed air driven machine called the 'Gartsherrie' in a mine near Coatbridge. It undercut the coal like a chain saw, but the inferior metals available at the time caused frequent breakdowns. Baird's stopped using and marketing it.

After the Gartsherrie, British manufacturers concentrated on developing machines which undercut the coal with a rotating disc, or a bar, like a drill-bit. The Americans however perfected chain cutters and reintroduced them to Britain about 1902. Many collieries started using them during the First World War and they became the most versatile and widely used machines.

Most of these were driven by electricity and Scottish companies were leaders in applying electrical engineering

THE "D.L." PATENT ELECTRIC COAL CUTTER.
Improved Longwall Machine. Direct or Alternating Current. Modern Design. First-class Construction.
CHAMBERS, SCOTT & Co,, MOTHERWELL.
ELECTRIC HAULAGE GEARS. WINCHES & CRANES.
SOLE AGENTS FOR THE "D.L." MACHINE—
FLETCHER, KILPATRICK & CO.,
Electrical Engineers, Pump and Engine Makers,
15, E. Vermont Street, Kinning Park, GLASGOW.
Telegrams—"COALPLANT, GLASGOW": "ENERGY, MOTHERWELL."

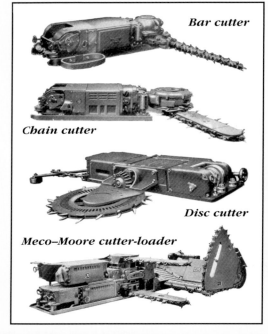

Bar cutter

Chain cutter

Disc cutter

Meco–Moore cutter-loader

to the mining industry. Mavor & Coulson of Glasgow, founded as electrical engineers Muir & Mavor in 1883, delivered their first electric coal-cutter to a Staffordshire colliery in 1898. Anderson Boyes of Motherwell were established in 1899 to supply complete electrical installations at collieries and electrically driven equipment, including coal cutters. The two companies eventually joined forces and continued to supply mining equipment until the late 1990s.

The increased used of coal-cutters meant that more coal was mined by a technique known as longwall advancing. In it the coal was cut from a face of about 150–200 yards long [137–183 metres] between parallel roads. Once the machine had sliced under the face, the coal was broken up by explosives and shovelled into hutches for transport to the surface. Conveyors were developed early in the twentieth century, to take coal from the face to hutches waiting in the roads.

Retreat mining, a variant of longwall advancing, was developed in the late nineteenth century and is widely used in modern mines. Parallel roads are driven to the limit of the area to be worked and the coal then worked back to the start point. The roads take longer to drive and require more maintenance, but geological problems are discovered before production begins and hold-ups minimised.

Using a chain cutter in a Fife colliery

A machine known as the AB Meco–Moore cutter-loader, which combined the functions of cutters and conveyors, was developed during the Second World War by Anderson Boyes and two other manufacturers. The machine and its face conveyor had to be manhandled forward after each cut, limiting its effect. Ironically the solution to this problem, the Armoured Flexible Conveyor [AFC], had also been developed during the war, but by the German mining industry! The AFC could be snaked forward with the cutter, allowing it to be

Hydraulic face-line supports and Armoured Flexible Conveyor

-cutters

Trepanner at Harviestoun mine, Clackmannanshire

applied continuously to the face. Machines known as shearers, which cut the coal with small picks on a revolving drum, were introduced in the 1950s. The size of drum could be varied according to the height of seam. Similar machines known as trepanners cut the coal end-on, producing larger lumps. The power-loaded faces worked by shearers and trepanners were protected by hydraulic face-line supports. These could be moved forward after each cut, along with the AFC. Some narrow and soft seams were worked using a plough which was hauled along the face by chain or rope, shaving off slices of coal. Machines known as continuous miners were used in stoop and room workings, and to drive roadways and headings.

Anderton shearer

Raising the flag on the new nationalised era

The Coal Industry Commission, set up after the First World War, recommended a form of nationalisation and although the government rejected it, the seed had been sown. Miners continued to fight for nationalisation, and the Labour Party campaigned for it in the 1945 general election. They won a landslide victory and the industry was nationalised on New Years' Day 1947. A National Coal Board [NCB] was set up to run it.

nationalisation

NCB

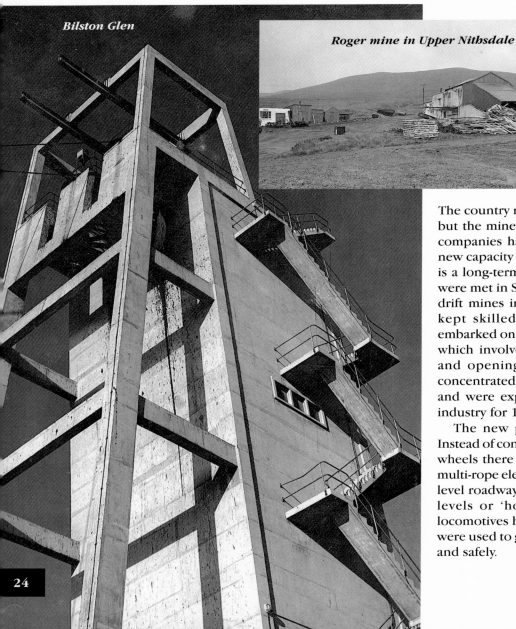

Bilston Glen

Roger mine in Upper Nithsdale

The country needed coal to rebuild after the war, but the mines were in poor shape. The old coal companies had begun some developments, but new capacity was urgently needed. Coal however is a long-term business and so short-term needs were met in Scotland by opening over forty small drift mines in known coalfield areas. They also kept skilled men employed while the NCB embarked on a massive development programme which involved redeveloping existing collieries and opening new ones. Most of these were concentrated in Fife, the Lothians and Ayrshire, and were expected to secure the future of the industry for 100 years.

The new pits changed the look of mining. Instead of conventional pit-head frames and pulley wheels there were concrete winding towers and multi-rope electric friction winders. Underground, level roadways were driven from the shafts at set levels or 'horizons'. These were worked by locomotives hauling mine cars. Man-riding trains were used to get men to and from the face quickly and safely.

24

There were two super-pits in Fife: Rothes, at Thornton—the 'jewel in the crown', and Seafield near Kirkcaldy. There were also new shafts and redevelopment schemes in Fife at Bowhill, Michael and Valleyfield collieries. A tunnel, driven under the Forth in the early 1960s, connected Valleyfield with the redeveloped Kinneil Colliery at Bo'ness. There were new super-pits at Monktonhall and Bilston Glen in the Lothians. In Ayrshire there was a major new sinking at Killoch and re-developments of Barony, Littlemill, Kames and Pennyvenie collieries. Britain's largest drift mine was opened at Glenochil, in Clackmannanshire and in Lanarkshire new shafts were sunk at Kingshill, Bedlay and Cardowan collieries.

Killoch

Seafield

Monktonhall

Rothes

the long decline

All these developments made the early 1950s an exciting time to be in mining, but the euphoria did not last. Oil and nuclear fuels began to make inroads into coal's expected markets and the old heavy coal-using industries began to wither and change. With falling demand and new high-profile developments adding to capacity, the NCB had to make hard choices. Seemingly viable pits were closed and, as production grew at the new pits, even more pits had to close. An unremitting struggle to match output with demand had begun. Sinking of another super-pit, at Airth in Stirlingshire, was begun in 1958, but markets were starting to fall off, and it was stopped. And then, some of the big developments failed. Sinking at Rothes hit water and geological difficulties and despite bringing some coal to the surface in 1957, and a visit from the Queen and Prince Philip a year later, the pit was abandoned in 1962. Glenochil Mine also closed at the same time. The old stoops it had been planned to work were found to be crushed and broken, and other seams could not be extracted economically.

The spiral of contraction continued. The last great miners' strike in 1984 was followed by the closure, or moth-balling, of all but one of the country's pits. It was privatised in 1995 along with the rest of the British coal industry.

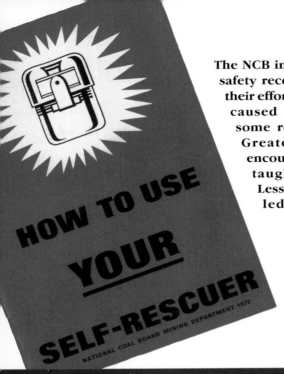

How to use YOUR SELF-RESCUER

NATIONAL COAL BOARD MINING DEPARTMENT 1972

The NCB improved the industry's poor safety record, with training central to their efforts. Accidents were not always caused by dangerous conditions, some resulted from bad practice. Greater safety awareness was encouraged, and training schools taught safe ways of working. Lessons learned from accidents led to new regulations and

SAFETY

improved equipment. The NCB expanded scientific research into dust control, and respiratory diseases like pneumoconiosis. Safer explosives were developed and improved methods of detecting firedamp [methane gas] were developed.

Naked flame lamps were replaced universally with electric battery lamps and headgear was improved: soft American canvas caps were replaced by compressed cardboard helmets and eventually plastic hard hats. Self rescuers, which gave men time to get out of danger, were introduced after forty-seven trapped men were killed by the smoke and fumes of a fire at Auchengeich Colliery, Chryston in 1959.

Award winning poster idea by Steve Haigh, a Deputy at Barnsley Main Colliery, North Yorkshire

Teaching prop setting

Mines Rescue

Coalowners Associations were required to establish Mines Rescue stations under the Coal Mines Act of 1911. Scotland's first station, at Cowdenbeath, was set up by the Fife and Clackmannan Coalowners Association in 1910—a year before the Act! Other stations followed at Kilmarnock in 1912, and Coatbridge and Edinburgh in 1915. Of these Coatbridge was Scotland's only permanently manned 'A' station, the others were known as 'B', or training, stations.

Scottish Mines Rescue men carried out one of the most remarkable rescues anywhere in the world when liquid peat flooded into Knockshinnoch Castle Colliery, New Cumnock, in 1950. It was a very Scottish type of disaster and it had happened before. Eight men died in 1901 when peat flooded Donibristle pit near Cowdenbeath, and in 1918, a similar flood killed nineteen at Stanrigg Colliery near Airdrie. Regulations should have prevented a repetition, but thirteen died when it happened again at Knockshinnoch. What made this disaster exceptional was the rescue of 116 trapped men who were brought to safety after forty-eight hours. The men came out in relays, through old gas-filled workings, using breathing apparatus that none of them were familiar with.

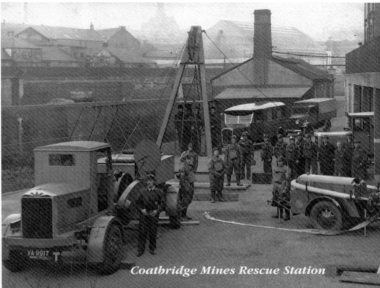

Coatbridge Mines Rescue Station

Knockshinnoch Castle Colliery

communication

The Knockshinnoch disaster differed from others in that the telephone still worked, making it possible for the rescuers and trapped men to communicate with each other. Prior to the development of the telephone the only communication between surface and underground was by runner. Bells were used to signal when cages were ready to be raised or lowered.

the continuing toll

1922 East Plean, Stirling—explosion; 12 dead.	1957 Kames, Muirkirk—explosion; 17 dead.
1923 Gartshore near Twechar—explosion; 8 dead.	1957 Lindsay, Fife—explosion; 9 dead.
1923 Redding, near Falkirk—flood; 40 dead.	1959 Auchengeich, Chryston—fire; 47 dead.
1931 Bowhill, Fife—explosion; 10 dead.	1967 Michael, East Wemyss—fire; 9 dead.
1938 Dumbreck, Kilsyth—electrical fire; 9 dead.	1973 Seafield, Kirkcaldy—roof fall; 5 dead.
1939 Valleyfield, Fife—explosion; 33 dead.	1982 Cardowan, Stepps—explosion; 41 injured.

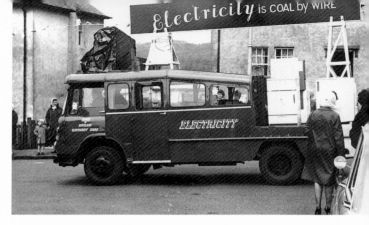

The one colliery still working in 1995 was part the NCB's big Scottish success story. It started with the opening, in 1960, of a new power station at Kincardine on Forth. The station could burn an inferior quality of coal, available from an adjacent and easily accessible seam known as the Upper Hirst. The coal industry had previously discounted the seam because of its high ash content, but now there was a market for it. The market grew when a neighbouring power station was proposed at Longannet in the early 1960s. By this time electricity generation was coal's fastest growing and most important market. Oil and gas were seen as likely fuels for the new station, but the NCB proposed a remarkable scheme

electricity-

to supply it with Upper Hirst coal. New mines, Solsgirth, Castlehill and Bogside, were developed with an underground conveyor running through them to take the coal directly to the new station. These mines looked unremarkable on the surface, but underground the engineering and the record-breaking output was spectacular. By the 1980s the workings were extending far from the mine openings and so a new shaft, Castlebridge, was sunk to the west of Castlehill, which gave access to the coal as it dipped to deeper levels. It was commissioned in 1986 and maintained production until 1999, by which time an area south of the Forth had been opened up to provide the power-station with coal for another twenty years.

Conveyor comes to the surface at Longannet mine

BARONY GENERATING STATION

SOUTH OF SCOTLAND ELECTRICITY BOARD

HEAD OFFICE
351 SAUCHIEHALL STREET, GLASGOW
TEL.: DOUGLAS 9955

opencast

Although Longannet is the largest of Scotland's coal-fired power stations, there are others, most notably Cockenzie in East Lothian. Modern stations like these burn coal at a very high temperature. It is blended from

Westfield opencast site

– 'Coal by Wire'

a variety of sources, powdered, mixed with pre-heated air and blown into the furnaces. The only Scottish coal going to these stations, other than Longannet's deep-mined reserves, comes from opencast sites. It as if mining has gone back in time to the days when coal was dug out of holes in the ground, but these new sites are vast and are worked, using quarrying, rather than mining, techniques.

Opencast sites produce huge amounts of coal, but are not worked for long and so their names do not become known in the way that many deep mines became household names. Many of the sites are in areas which were once deep mined and old workings are often exposed. At Dalquhandy, near Coalburn, an old coal-cutter was unearthed which is now in the Scottish Mining Museum.

Lochore Meadows Country Park

Lochore Meadows Country Park

environmental impact

Opencasting is more economical than deep mining, although it can have a significant environmental impact which the site operators strive to minimise by reinstating the land when they have finished.

The impact of old mine sites is mixed. Subsidence can still damage buildings, although when it occurs in open country the lowered ground can fill with water to become a boggy wet-land habitat for wildlife. Elsewhere old workings, which have filled up with mine water can overflow, pollute and discolour adjacent water courses. Many old bings have been removed to provide road-making materials or been landscaped into grass, or tree-covered mounds. One of the most successful reclamation projects in Scotland was the creation of Lochore Meadows Country Park in central Fife.

The monasteries, which controlled much of the country's wealth, were dissolved during the Reformation of 1560 and landowners took over the coal workings. They sought to make a profit from them and worked people hard; some paid good wages, others did not. There was widespread poaching of experienced workers and a kind of commercial anarchy replaced the old, stable order of monastic patronage. By 1606 the coal and salt industries were in such disarray that the Scottish Parliament passed an Act to regulate them:

a race apart

ACT ANENT coilzearis and Saltaris

OURE SOUERANE LORD and estaittis of this present parliament Statutis and ordinis that na person within this realme heireftir shall fie, hyre or conduce, ony salteris, Coilzearis, or coilberaris without ane sufficient testimoniall of thair Maister quhome they Last seruit, subscryuit with his hand, or at least sufficient attestation of ane ressonable cause of thair removeing maid in the presence of ane baillie or magistrat of the pairt quhair they come fra. And in case ony ressaue, fie, hyre, supplie or Interteny ony of the saidis, colzearis, salteris or coilberaris without ane sufficient testimonie as said is, The Maisteris quhome fra they came challengeing their servandis within yeir and day. That the pairtie quhome fra they ar challengeit Sall delyuer thame bak agane within tuentie four houris under the pane of ane hundreth pundis to be payit to the persones quhome fra they passit, And that for ilk person and ilk tyme that they or ony of thame salhappin to be challengeit and not deliyuerit as said is. And the saidis coilzearis, coilberaris and saltaris to be estemit repute and halden as theiffis and punischit in their bodyes, viz, samony of thame as shall ressaue foirwageis and feis. And the saidis Estaittis of this present paliment Gevis gives power and Comissioun to all maisteris and awneris of coilheughis and pannis To apprehend all vagabonds and sturdie beggeris to be put to labour.

They belonged, like the serfs of an older time, to their respective works, with which they were sold as part of the gearing.
Henry Cockburn in *Memorials of His Time* (1800).

It may have been an attempt to outlaw breach of contract and stabilise the industry, but it had the effect of making colliers, salters and coalbearers into slaves. They could not leave their work without written authority—which was unlikely to be given—and they were regarded as having stolen their bodies if they left without permission. Anyone enticing them away from their employer, would be heavily fined. Vagrants could also be forced to work in coal mines or salt pans.

The word 'collier' at that time referred to someone who worked coal, whereas 'miner' was used to describe a man who extracted metal ore, like gold, silver or lead. Miners endured a form of slavery too, as did mill workers and farm servants, but the colliers suffered worst and came to be seen as a race apart. They were bound for life to a dirty, dangerous, unpleasant job and sometimes to a hard master, working underground for long hours in conditions most people could only guess at. Almost permanently dirty, some lived in towns along with other people, but many lived in isolated communities in often squalid housing. They paid no taxes and received some money as well as payments in kind, like coal and candles.

Such employment conditions were unlikely to attract willing recruits and so the industry relied on a system called 'arling', in which parents pledged their childrens' future work to the coal-owner in return for money. It was like selling them into slavery. Children worked in mines from a very early age—the more working children a man had, the more coal he could win. Some miners exploited their own children's labour.

slave's collar

'truly, they were slaves'

In 1842, over 40 years after they were freed, two old miners recalled the injustices of serfdom

---

Walter Pryde, 81:

I was first yoked to the coal work at Preston Grange when I was nine years of age.

Even if we had no work on the colliery . . . we could seek none other without a written license and agreement to return. Even then the laird or the tacksman selected our place of work, and if we did not do his bidding we were placed by the necks in iron collars called juggs, and fastened to the wall, 'or made to go the rown'. The latter I recollect well, the men's hands were tied in face of the horse at the gin and made to run backwards all day.

Robert Ingles, 82:

I was born 9th Sept. 1759 and worked at Pinkie Pit before the colliers got their freedom.

Father and grandfather were slaves to the laird of Preston Grange and after the works had stopped . . . we could not get work as the neighbours kenned that the Laird of Preston Grange would send the sheriff after us and bring us back.

So binding was the bondage, that the lairds had the power of taking colliers who had left them out of His Majesty's ships, or bringing back any who had enlisted in the army.

. . . the work done by slaves, though it appears to cost only their maintenance is, in the end, the dearest of any.

Adam Smith in *The Wealth of Nations* (1776).

Great houses reflect the wealth, power and influence of the eighteenth century coal-owning landowners. But, as time wore on, their bonded colliers became a liability. They had become a small, closed community of unwilling serfs who had learned to do only as much as was needed to survive. As they began to demand high wages costs rose and profits dropped. Scottish coal-owners paid more for less output than Northumbrian mine owners who employed free men without difficulty. In Scotland the industry could only recruit unwilling vagrants and was stagnating for lack of labour, retarding other industrial development. Parliament tried to improve this in 1775, by removing the condition that tied a man to a colliery if he worked there for a year and a day. It made little difference and in 1799 another Act was passed which finally freed miners from slavery. But the problem got worse before it got better. Miners, released from bondage,

left the pits in droves, to taste freedom at half the wages! New recruits to the industry preferred surface work to hewing coal and recovery only started when economic necessity drew men back to the pits.

The Marquis of Lothian's Newbattle Abbey
Glasgow Museums and Archives

The 1830s were a time of political upheaval in Britain. The Combination Laws had been repealed in 1824, allowing unions to be formed, and the Reform Act of 1832 gave more people the vote. Power was slipping from landowners who tried to embarrass the rising capitalist class by highlighting the plight of children in mines and factories. Parliament's response was to set up the Children's Employment Commission in 1840; in Scotland it embarrassed the old aristocracy.

The Commissioners had to report on conditions for women as well as children and they sought evidence from all over the country. In the west of Scotland they found that women no longer worked underground: the result of union opposition and mining companies introducing new working practices. So, for evidence of female and child employment, the Commissioners went east, to the pits owned by the great landowners—and the further east, the worse the conditions got. The Commissioners interviewed thousands of people. What they saw and heard horrified them.

Children's Employment

Margaret Hipps, 17:

My employment . . . is to fill a bagie, or slype, with two and a half hundredweight to three hundredweight of coal. I then hook it on to my chain and drag it through the seam which is 26—28 inches high, till I get to the main road—a good distance, probably 200–400 yards. The pavement I drag over is wet and I am obliged at all times to crawl on hands and feet with my bagie hung to the chains and ropes.

It is sad, sweating and sore fatiguing work, and frequently maims the women.

Jane Watson, 40:

I have wrought in the bowels of the earth thirty-three years. Have been married twenty-three years and had nine children; six are alive, three died of typhus a few years since; have had two dead born; thinks they were so from oppressive work; a vast number of women have dead children and false births which are worse as they are no able to work after the latter.

I have always been obliged to work below till forced to go home to bear the bairn and so have all the other women.

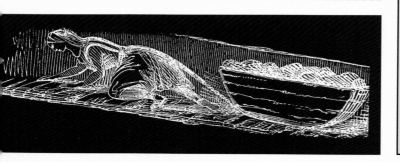

NOTICE.
NO FEMALES

Permitted, on any account, to work under ground at this Colliery; and all such is STRICTLY PROHIBITED, by Orders from His Grace the Duke of Hamilton.

JOHN JOHNSTON, Overseer.

REDDING COLLIERY, 4th March, 1845.   J. Duncan, Printer, Falkirk.

Jane Kerr, 12:

I get up at three in the morning and gang to the work at four, return at four and five at night.

The ladder pit in which I work is gai drippie and the air is kind of bad as the lamps do not burn so bright as in guid air. Accidents frequently happen from the tugs breaking and the loads falling on those behind.

My father straps me when I do not do his bidding.

Commission

Parliament was so shocked by the Commission's report it quickly passed the Mines Act of 1842. It was a major social change. Women and girls, and boys under ten were banned from working underground, and mines inspectors were introduced to ensure the laws were being obeyed. Subsequent parliamentary acts raised the age limit for boys. Some women feared the loss of money would drive them further into poverty and unsuccessfully petitioned Parliament to let them work as before. Others continued to go underground, dressed as men.

There was little comfort for men in the new laws—if anything they had to work harder to make up the money lost to the family. The exercise therefore gave the union movement a boost as miners rejected the parliamentary process and turned to more direct action to achieve improvements in wages and conditions.

Brothers John and Thomas Duncan worked as trappers—boys who sat for hours in the dark, opening and closing ventilation trap doors to allow the tubs of coal to pass:

Thomas, 11:

I open the air-doors for the putters from six in the morning 'till six at night. Mother calls me up at five in the morning and gives me a piece of cake [oatcake], which is all I get 'till I return. There is plenty of water in the pit; the part I am in it comes up to my knees.

John, 10:

Where I sit is very wet. We never change our clothes nor go to school, but we go to the kirk sometimes when we have clean clothes.

Robert Robinson, 14:

Would not have gone so early to work but father died of the black spittle, he was off work twelve months before death and spit his lungs up all as black as ink; he was not fifty years old.

After father's death mother sent younger brother and two sisters below.

My two sisters were sair horrible crashed by stones falling from the roof; their bowels were forced out and legs broken, and both died soon after.

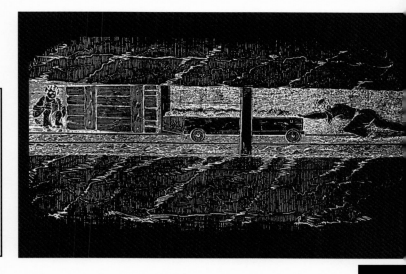

The industry had to adapt to the requirements of the Mines Act of 1842: one of the most obvious changes being the increased number of ponies working underground, to replace the child and female bearers outlawed by the Act. Subsequent laws governing the mining industry brought other changes, but the improvements were gradual and the miner's daily dice with discomfort, dirt and danger carried on as before. Then as now, the media were fascinated by the big explosions, fires and floods. Rock falls, runaway hutches and shaft incidents, however, took a greater toll and rated fewer column inches in newspapers while small injuries like cuts, bruises and broken bones passed without comment. Roof falls were common and could happen without warning. The crashing sound and rush of displaced air could be terrifying. If a fall cut off escape routes a buildup of gas could overcome the trapped men and it was a race against time to clear the obstruction.

Mines were never comfortable places to work in; they could be hot, dry, dusty, or wet, and the water in mines tended to be very cold. The experience of sharing an unnatural and inherently dangerous environment bound men together. The men relied on each other and developed mutual respect, if not always a liking; aggression was also part of the culture. Humour too helped men to survive and miners enjoyed playing practical jokes on each other.

Miners also shared their workplace with rats, mice and insects, and sometimes rats got to the miners' 'pieces' first. With no underground canteen, men had to eat where they worked, with dirty hands. The fillings of miner's pieces were unlikely to gain a gourmet star rating: cheese, cheese and lemon curd, cheese and jam, chocolate bar, dripping, spam or some other delight. The piece tin was shaped like a plain loaf, with one end rounded and the other square. It held three sandwiches and if a piece of toast was included, it apparently kept the other bread fresh. Pieces that had been down a pit were said to taste good, and when men came back up, they were chivvied by children for any they had left.

all in a

Miners had to keep their mouths moist and took a flask of water or cold sweet tea down with them. Ponies were said to have been able to learn how to open a miner's piece tin or take the stopper out of his flask. The men also chewed tobacco or sucked sweets, or even bits of coal!

There were no toilets in older mines. Men found a measure of privacy in old workings—and covered the offending results with a stone. Others used coal dust on a shovel to propel human waste into the old workings. Smells could be carried through the pit and it was always wise to check the direction of the ventilation airflow first!

Wet workings at Canderrigg Colliery, Lanarkshire

day's work

It took many people to operate a large pit during the industry's boom years. Managers, engineers and surveyors had duties above and below ground. Shankers, who did the dangerous job of maintaining the shaft, or shank, worked between the pit bottom and the surface; others worked entirely on the surface. When the coal came up from the pit it had to be weighed—and check-weighed by a man employed by the miners to ensure they were not being cheated, picked clean of stone, washed and loaded into wagons. Once in the wagons it was evenly distributed, or 'trimmed' and taken to sidings by locomotive drivers and shunters.

Miners on a cage

Pit bottomers

Underground haulage

pit work

Blacksmiths sharpened picks and shoed horses. They had to maintain, or sometimes make, pit equipment and, as technology improved, they were joined by other skilled tradesmen like mechanics and electricians. The real aristocrat amongst surface workers was the winding-engineman who had to ensure safe operation of the cages at all times.

Although the pit worked round the clock, much of the time was spent keeping it in good order. One group of men prepared the face by undercutting it and boring shot-holes for the facemen. Drawers and putters worked with the face men loading hutches and taking them to the roadways where pony drivers or haulage systems took them to the pit bottom. There, more men put the hutches on the cages and sent them to the surface.

All this activity pushed the workings further from the shaft, and men were employed to extend the roadways which served the coal faces. Others developed new working places for the facemen, and maintenance men, not engaged in coalface work, ensured that rail tracks and haulage ropes were in good order. Repairers looked after roadways, re-supporting and extending them where needed. People above and below ground, not engaged in coalface work, were known as 'oncost' workers, because coal was priced at the face and the cost of their wages was added on before it was sold.

Brushers preparing a coal face

mining jobs:

Manager—responsible for output, maintenance and safety.

Oversman—the manager's underground deputy.

Fireman—ensures that the workings are free of gas and safe to work in.

Winding-engineman—operates the huge engine that raises and lowers the cage.

Blacksmith—sharpens miners' picks, shoes ponies and repairs or makes pit equipment.

Collier [miner]—gets the coal.

Shot firer—breaks the coal seam with explosives.

Brusher—removes 'redd' [loose rock] and enlarges roadways, using explosives.

Reddsman—clears loose rock from the roads.

Pit-bottomer—loads hutches on and off cages and supervises men going on the cage.

Banksman—does the same job at the surface.

Picker—often female, picks out lumps of stone from the coal on a conveyor.

Shanker—sinks and maintains shaft—wears special hat, lamp protector and cape to keep dry.

Driver—often a boy on his first job drives, and looks after, a pony.

Drawers and Putters—move the coal from the face to the haulage roads in hutches.

the unions

Alexander McDonald

Miners, freed from slavery, found that 'combination laws' prohibited the formation of unions, but when these were repealed in 1824, small pit-based unions began to form. They grew into district unions and in 1841 a single national union, the Miners' Association of Great Britain [MAGB] was formed. It collapsed a few years later when strikes against wage cuts failed.

At the time a young miner named Alexander McDonald was studying at Glasgow University. He had begun working alongside his father in a Lanarkshire mine, in 1830, when he was only nine years old. Never losing his thirst for knowledge, he continued his education as best he could and saved enough money to go to university. In what spare time he had from his studies, he worked underground to earn more money to pay the fees and graduated in 1848 soon after the collapse of the MAGB.

After graduation McDonald worked as a teacher and invested his money to provide an income. He became secretary of the Holytown miners, emerging as a leader after a failed strike in 1856 and playing a significant role in the drafting of the Mines Regulation Act of 1860. This provided for check-weighers to ensure miners' coal was accurately weighed.

McDonald worked to establish a national union, sought improvements through reduced darg [the amount of work done in a day] and promoted emigration schemes to cut the size of the labour force. Under his influence a 'stay-down' strike in Fife, when the men refused to come to the surface, won the first eight hour working day.

By 1870 McDonald was the acknowledged leader of the British miners, although there was no national union. The Mines Act of 1872 legislated for many of the causes he had championed: union recognition, improvements to hours, wages and safety. He became Liberal MP for Stafford in 1874 and continued to campaign for the miners' cause until his death in 1881.

Alexander McDonald

Hardie with George Bernard Shaw

organise
Keir Hardie

J. Keir Hardie, M.P.

J. Kein Hardie 1905

One of the younger men inspired by McDonald's example was James Keir Hardie who started work in 1866 when he was 10 years old, as a trapper in a Lanarkshire pit. In his early twenties he was involved in union activities and organised a strike against wage cuts. The mine owners banned him from pit work.

He moved to Cumnock in 1880 to become Organising Secretary of the Ayrshire Miners, but when a ten week strike failed, the beaten union had no money to pay him. Calling himself 'Trapper' he started writing a column in the *Cumnock News* called 'Black Diamonds'. It campaigned openly for the miners. In 1887 he launched a monthly journal called *The Miner*.

Disillusioned with the Liberal Party he fought the Mid-Lanark by-election in 1888 arguing for the formation of a Labour Party. The new Scottish Labour Party was formed later that year and Hardie became its secretary and driving force. He was adopted as a candidate for South West Ham in London in 1891, and became the first MP to represent the Labour movement. He was now a national figure and was made chairman of the new Independent Labour Party when it was formed in 1893.

He changed the title of *The Miner* to the *Labour Leader* in 1894, but lost his seat in Parliament the following year. In 1900, he was elected MP for Merthyr Tydfil and represented this constituency for the rest of his life. After the 1906 election the Labour group in parliament became the Labour Party and Hardie was made its leader. He died in 1915 at the age of fifty-nine.

Scotland's first 'county' union was formed in Fife; others followed and in 1894 they formed the Scottish Miners' Federation. This became affiliated to the Miners' Federation of Great Britain [MFGB], also in 1894, and later that year 70,000 men went on strike. Police broke up gatherings, the leadership quarrelled, the owners refused to negotiate and the strike collapsed, although the Fife men held out for seventeen weeks before they too were defeated.

first national strike

Why have fifty mine owners power to starve 70,000 miners into submission?

Keir Hardie (1894).

While output and manpower in the pits grew, union membership fell, and fell again after more wage cuts in 1895 and 1896. Conciliation Boards were set up throughout Britain to regulate wages. As coal prices rose, so did wages, but they fell along with prices too. It was not ideal. In 1909 the owners proposed a wage cut and threatened a 'lockout', to stop the men from working unless they accepted. The Conciliation Boards were sidelined as negotiations dragged on and the relative peace that had lasted for almost a decade was in jeopardy. In 1911 the MFGB demanded a fair minimum wage. The government, alarmed at the worsening situation, intervened and suggested a resolution at district rather than at national level. The idea found favour with neither side and the first ever national strike began on 1st March 1912. It lasted six weeks and although gains were small, the miners had brought the industry to a standstill and learned the value of acting nationally. They were now a force to be reckoned with.

Gathering coal during 1912 strike

GATHERING COALS at WOODILEE PIT HEAD. 1912

immigrants

Lithuanian shop at Bellshill, Lanarkshire
North Lanarkshire Council

Mining in Scotland offered hope to people suffering poverty, starvation or persecution in their native lands. The first immigrants came from Ireland in the 1830s and 40s, attracted by the expansion of coal and iron in Lanarkshire and Ayrshire. The influx continued throughout the nineteenth century as the mining industry expanded. Local people, fearing job losses, were hostile, but reserved their worst prejudice for the Lithuanians, thousands of whom fled from Russian persecution in the late nineteenth century. Many headed for America, but some arrived in Scotland looking for work. They found it in mines and iron works, and the tiny, damp house that went with it was, for them, a bonus. The largest communities were around Bellshill in Lanarkshire and Glengarnock in Ayrshire. Lithuanians were accused of being strike breakers, of living in squalor, and because they spoke little English, of being a danger to others! Worse, everybody called them 'Poles'. Some collieries called them by numbers, others gave them names like Green, Brown or Smith, as if learning their real names was too much bother.

Spanish and Portuguese labourers arrived in Ayrshire in the early twentieth century along with shipments of ironstone brought into Scotland after local supplies had run out. Men of other European nationalities, who settled in Scotland after the Second World War, were also recruited into the mining industry.

Cronberry store, Ayrshire

Allanton, Hamilton

Fallin, Stirlingshire

Coaltown of Wemyss

New housing at Twechar, Dunbartonshire, in the 1920s

Alexander McDonald described miners' houses in Scotland as being 'in many cases no better than pigsties'. His campaign for their improvement was taken up by the *Glasgow Herald* which published a series of investigative reports in 1875. The reporter trusting his own eyes, and in some cases his nose, braved all weathers tramping through bogs and along railway lines to get at the truth. His reports were damning.

Lumphinnans, Fife

At Netherton, near Anniesland, Glasgow he found that, 'Damp walls and imperfect light and ventilation combine to render the apartment a nursery for disease'. Along the road at Blairdardie there were 'two beds . . . but . . . one is rendered useless by the dampness of the walls'. At Carfin he found 'especially foul' water with 'worms and wee creepers . . . in it in summer'. He found ashpits near Holytown that were 'an offence to all decency' and reported 'several cases of fever and smallpox'. He wondered, 'that epidemic is not always rife in Jerviston Square', while Mossend's Briggate 'is an exaggeration of all that is evil in miners' dwellings'. 'The ashpits and closets' at Rawyards near Airdrie were 'filthy in the extreme and the road in front of the houses is a dirty puddle'. In Clackmannan the houses at the Pottery were 'extremely unhealthy' and 'hardly possible that [they] should ever be dry'. And at Westfield 'no fewer than ten persons [were] living in a small room and kitchen'. At Newtongrange, however, the reporter found 'capital dwellings in . . . a well ordered village'.

The Lothian Coal Company expanded Newtongrange to accommodate over 6500 people, when the Lady Victoria Colliery was opened in the 1890s. It was regarded as a 'model' village and a Royal Commission on Housing in Scotland, set up after the 1912 strike, described its houses as 'probably the best built for miners in Scotland'.

Another such 'model' village' was Coaltown of Wemyss in Fife—old mining villages in the east of Scotland were often known as 'coal towns'. Coaltown of Wemyss was originally two villages, Easter and Wester Coaltown, which became one in the 1890s. It was developed by the Wemyss Coal Company when they sunk their new Lochhead pit and increased exports through Methil Docks. The population almost doubled from 381 to 731. As well as houses and shops there was a school and a school of needlework. Lady Eva Wemyss also set up the 'Earl David' pub as a charitable project in 1911.

In the 1950s, while the NCB was developing its large new collieries, it was also closing pits in the old Lanarkshire heartland. This meant that the people were not where the work was and so the Coal Board embarked on what it believed to be one of the largest movements of people in Scotland's history. New towns were planned, but despite being a better standard of houses than those in the old miners' rows, many people were reluctant to move. It meant forsaking all the familiar things: friends, neighbours, pub, club and football team. Some people were also fearful that they would be jumping the queue and depriving local people of a house, but eventually thousands of people moved.

A large family meant there was always someone able to earn money. It gave parents security for their old age. This Irish father and Scottish mother from 1900 were typical. They had ten children; eight survived to work in the pits, although the baby left through ill health. The boy behind his father was a 'tramp brusher' moving from job to job, getting paid by the day, 'on the shovel'. His brother, to the right, was forced out of the pits through ill health made worse by working in wet conditions. The eldest son's career was cut short by nystagmus, an eye disorder caused by working in the dim light of safety lamps. The boy on the right became a fireman and rescue brigadesman. The girls all worked at the picking tables from the day they left school to the day they married; and had large families!

A young woman could work on the surface, as a picker, but once married she was thirled to washing, cleaning, cooking and bringing up numerous children. Her day was arranged around the men's working day. She had to make up their pieces and, when they returned from the pit, have a hot meal waiting for them, and plenty of hot water for their bath in front of the kitchen range. Women took pride in keeping their house clean and tidy—not easy with coal dust all around and the atmosphere full of soot. They also scrubbed the front step and made sure the 'sheugh' [communal drain], was cleared and cleaned. The communal wash-house was shared by four or more cottages and each housewife had an allocated day when it was her turn to wash the clothes, after which the children were often dunked in the hot water and given a good scrub. Life was hard, but there was a strong sense of sharing and community in mining villages.

Children from mining communities could grow up in the countryside or on the streets of industrial towns. Few villages had community facilities until the 1920s and so children had to make their own entertainment.

Street games were popular, as was football—there were so many children in some villages that teams from different rows could play against each other. At holiday time the ponies were brought to the surface and children could make a fuss of them and ride on them at gala days. These popular occasions involved the crowning of the 'Queen', followed by a parade through the village and competitions in the park. Families encouraged children to do well at school, so that they could escape to a better life.

When the pit siren blew to signal a disaster, women and children could do nothing except wait for news. They gathered anxiously at the pit-head, stranded between agony and hope, in the terrible knowledge that loved ones were in peril, not far away, but out of reach. Families who lost their breadwinner could also lose their home, because the mining company needed it for new miners coming in to replace those lost. Bereaved families faced destitution and money was often collected to help them. These collections were well supported after big disasters, but less so after single fatalities.

family life

ILLUSTRATED

MEET EVAN JONES, MINER

F.D.R's WIFE

ILLUSTRATED visits Mrs. Roosevelt

The social wellbeing of mining communities was bolstered by the setting up of the Miner's Welfare Fund in 1920. It was raised from a penny levied on every ton of coal, and contributions from mine workers. The money had to be spent in the areas where it came from and local committees, made up of management and men, decided what they wanted—Ayrshire favoured convalescent homes, others preferred institutes. These usually had halls, while some included games rooms and libraries. One, at Shotts, had a swimming pool. Outdoor facilities like bowling greens, play parks, tennis courts and recreation grounds also formed part of some schemes.

After Nationalisation, the NCB took over industrial welfare and a new body, the Coal Industry Social Welfare Organisation [CISWO] was set up to look after social welfare. It was incorporated as a limited company in 1952 managed jointly by the unions and NCB. There were around 200 institutes when CISWO came into being, but this number was reduced as the industry contracted, allowing the organisation to focus more on personal welfare. CISWO became a Registered Charity in 1995 when the industry was privatised.

Miners' Institute at Cowdenbeath

miners'

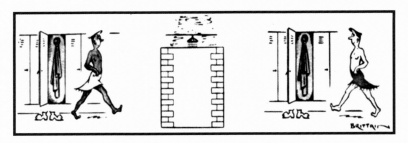

baths

The Miners' Welfare Fund was extended by a second levy in 1926 for the purpose of building pit-head baths. Some companies already provided baths and these had established the pattern of having showers placed between two sets of lockers. Miners coming up from the pit would put their dirty clothes in one locker, wash, and then go to the other locker room where they had left their clean clothes at the start of the shift. The NCB sold cut-price soap stamped PHB [pit-head baths].

Canteen at Killoch Colliery, Ayrshire

welfare

canteens & first aid

Baths buildings often had first aid rooms for the treatment of minor injuries, rooms where boots could be cleaned and facilities for filling water bottles at the start of the shift.

When the NCB took over, they continued to provide canteens. These had been made compulsory for large pits during the Second World War. They also set up fully staffed medical facilities at some large pits.

FIT AGAIN

Rehabilitation for Injured Miners
Uddingston Out-Patients' Centre
MINERS WELFARE COMMISSION

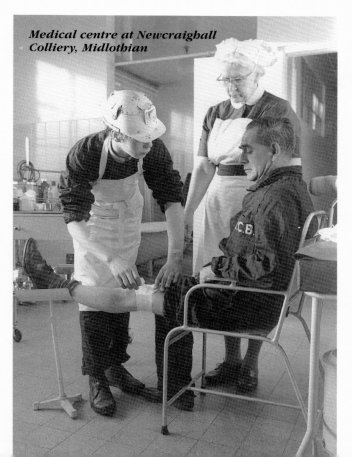

Medical centre at Newcraighall Colliery, Midlothian

dealing with serious injury

The Lanarkshire Orthopaedic Association began holding rehabilitation clinics for injured miners in the 1930s. The idea was adopted nationally during the Second World War when there was an urgent need to keep skilled men at work. It resulted in the Miners' Welfare Commission setting up a rehabilitation centre at Gleneagles Hotel in 1942. It was moved to a disused miners' welfare hall in the Viewpark area of Uddingston in 1945. There were medical treatment rooms, a gymnasium and sports facilities. Injured miners attended on a daily basis. They were given personal treatment regimes to return them to fitness. These included chores like gardening and sawing logs. The men could also hone their underground skills on a mock-up coal face. Badly injured men learned alternative skills so that they could return to as full and active a life as possible. Similar rehabilitation work was done at the Astley Ainslie Hospital in Edinburgh.

The Industrial and Providential Societies Act of 1893 allowed the proceeds of drink, sold in cooperative pubs, to be used to provide civic amenities. It was a Swedish idea, so the pubs were called Gothenburgs—Goths for short. They were austere drinking dens intended to reform men's drinking habits—or profit from them. They were not confined to mining areas, but were popular with mining companies, particularly in the east of Scotland, who could refuse to allow other pubs to be set up in their villages. They could also use proceeds from the Goth to provide amenities they would otherwise have to fund themselves. The first Scottish Goth was established by the Fife Coal Company at Hill o' Beath, and it soon paid for electric light in the village. Eventually there were about twenty Goths in Fife, with others in the Lothians and Stirlingshire.

gothenburg pubs

Inside a 'Goth' at Dean Tavern, Newtongrange

The buildings were bleak; gambling, music, dancing and games, including dominoes, were disallowed. Credit was prohibited. Managers were 'disinterested' in that they had no personal incentive to make a profit for themselves. There was also a strong temperance element to the idea and the money earned from drink at some Goths was used to set up libraries, reading rooms and rooms for the sale of food and nonalcoholic beverages.

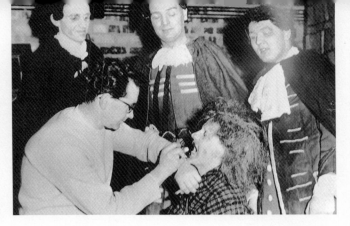

Mining communities, which were often isolated from main population centres, were good at providing their own entertainment. Most institutes had large, well equipped halls, ideal for travelling entertainers and performances of music or drama by local people. A number of miners, who started at local shows, went on to become famous stars.

The Rigside players prepare for a drama competition
Coal Industry Social Welfare Organisation

after work

Sir Harry Lauder worked in pits in the Hamilton area and, for a time, alternated between pit work and the stage until he was well enough known to become a full-time entertainer. He never forgot his early years working with pit-ponies and used his position in society to campaign for their better treatment.

Another world-renowned miner-turned-entertainer was accordionist and band leader Sir Jimmy Shand. One of Scotland's finest character comedians, Jack Radcliffe, from Cleland in Lanarkshire, also started life in the pits. Bill McCue was an electrician at the Kingshill pits near Shotts. He was awarded a Coal Industry Social Welfare Organisation [CISWO] grant to help him study at the Royal Academy of Music in London, and went on to become one of Scotland's finest and most versatile singers.

Joe Corrie was a Fife miner who began writing sketches, articles and poetry in the early 1920s for a local, radical, newspaper. During the 1926 strike he started to write plays which were highly regarded and became widely performed at drama festivals. In the days before television, amateur drama was a very popular form of home-grown entertainment in mining areas. Drama groups put on a variety of performances in local halls, but made a special effort for the fiercely contested inter-area competitions organised by CISWO.

A Joe Corrie play in performance

Sir Harry Lauder

Dancers at a gala at Ravenscraig Park, Dysart

Cowdenbeath band dressed for the weather at Holyrood Park

Gala days were festive occasions when mining families got together to enjoy music and sport and listen to rousing speeches. Some began as small pit-based sports, or children's play-days. Many had their origins in famous struggles; the Fife miners' gala began in June 1871 to celebrate the securing of the eight hour working day the previous year. It merged in 1947 with the annual Scottish miners' gala which was held annually, on 1st May, at Holyrood Park in Edinburgh. This began with a parade to the park, through the city streets, and was just like the small galas, only bigger. There were band competitions and sports like athletics, football and boxing. A Coal Queen, who had to work in the industry, or be the wife or daughter of a miner, was crowned. Children took pony rides—like the old days when pit-ponies were brought to the surface during holidays. Stalls were set up in a large marquee to sell produce, including craft goods made by disabled miners. There was dancing, and there were speeches from union leaders, politicians and celebrities.

galas & bands

Pipe or silver bands held pride of place at gala days. They headed the processions and took part in keenly contested competitions. Some bands were formed by the men of a town or village while the larger pits were able to muster enough men to form their own bands.

Weekly contributions from all the men who worked at the pit and fund-raising by voluntary committees paid for the band. Miners' bands were often very good and took part in national competitions, which they often won!

Gala float at Loanhead, Midlothian

'Dugs'

. . . and 'doos'

after work

Sport, and the great outdoors, offered an escape from pit life. Some men preferred a gentle walk on the moors, perhaps also doing a little poaching, others raced 'doos' [pigeons], or 'dugs' [dogs]. Football was also popular, as were quoiting, bowls, boxing and handball.

sports & pastimes

Football was the most popular miners' sport, with local rivalries as fierce as anything between Rangers and Celtic and the game was one of the best escape routes out of the pits. The legendary 'Slim' Jim Baxter played for Crossgates Primrose in Fife and Bill Shankly, the manager of Liverpool played for Glenbuck Cherrypickers from Ayrshire. Other ex-mining greats include Sir Matt Busby, Jock Stein, Eric Caldow and Willie Waddell. Willie Bauld of Hearts and Scotland was one of many who played for Newtongrange Star and later made their names in senior ranks.

Quoiting, pronounced 'kiteing', was a game for strong men who hurled a heavy iron ring at a peg stuck in a three foot square bed of clay. Great skill and considerable strength was needed. The quoiting 'green' was usually near a pub.

A lot of money could be staked on the outcome of most sports; almost anything that moved could have a bet placed on it. The biggest gambling game however was pitch and toss; two coins thrown in the air and a weeks' wages, or the holiday money, won or lost on the way they landed. It was illegal and boys enjoyed the excitement, and extra pocket-money earned by acting as lookouts.

Football match at Holyrood Park

A Royal Commission, set up in 1919 to investigate the industry, recommended, among other things, a form of nationalisation, but the government rejected this. It then compounded the industry's difficulties by suddenly abandoning wartime control of coal prices. The mine owners, left to pay high wages on low returns, offered the miners terms which amounted to a big cut in wages. These were rejected and the men went on strike in 1921. The dispute lasted for three bitter months and ended with the miners going back to low wages and high unemployment.

Unrest simmered for the next four years, but as the industry struggled to balance the books, pressure grew for another wage cut. A last-minute coal subsidy in 1925 only succeeded in delaying trouble, and on Friday May 1st 1926 the miners went on strike. The following Monday the General Strike of all trade unions began. It lasted for nine days, but the miners continued their strike for seven months. It was a bitter dispute and it ended, for the unions, with nothing gained. Unemployment in the industry rose to 40 per cent.

unions

Rival unions struggled for supremacy through the 1930s, but strength lay in unity and on 1st January 1945 the National Union of Mineworkers [NUM] was formed. Six months later Labour won a landslide General Election victory, and by the end of the year presented the Nationalisation Act to Parliament.

The NUM and NCB worked closely in the early years of Nationalisation, but a number of small disputes arose throughout the 1960s, when hard decisions over pit closures had to be made. In 1972 the NUM went on strike in pursuit of a wage claim and the Conservative government conceded an increase. The gains were quickly eroded by high inflation exacerbated by a world oil crisis. The union imposed an overtime ban in November 1973 and, in an attempt to preserve coal stocks, the Government introduced a three-day working week across the country. But when negotiations broke down in February 1974, another strike began. The government's response was to call a General Election which it lost. The incoming Labour government settled the miners' claim.

Margaret Thatcher became Prime Minister in 1979. Her government legislated to end NCB subsidies, but backed down in 1981 when the union threatened to strike over pit closures. Coal production was increased, and stocks accumulated. A new NCB Chairman, Ian MacGregor, was appointed in 1983 with instructions to run the industry without a subsidy—at the time over £900 million. In March 1984 the NCB announced the closure of Cortonwood, South Yorkshire, and Polmaise Collieries. Local strikes began and were declared 'official' by the NUM executive, under its new chairman Arthur Scargill. The executive called a national strike to support the local action, but did not hold a strike ballot and some pits continued to work. Stockpiles at pit-heads and power stations remained high though and the police had new trade union laws to enforce. The strike dragged on for a year, ending officially on 5th March 1985. Within five years all but one of Scotland's pits had been closed or mothballed.

Soup kitchen, Cowdenbeath, during 1921 strike

Two other unions represented people with management or supervisory duties. They were the National Association of Colliery Oversmen, Deputies and Shotfirers who were responsible for enforcing safety regulations underground, and the British Association of Colliery Management. The Colliery Office Staff Association was affiliated to the NUM.

1919–1985

Outdoor meeting on Ness Braes, Buckhaven, during 1926 strike

three Scottish leaders

Robert Smillie

Abe Moffat

Mick Megahey

53

Lady Victoria

The Lothian Coal Company was formed in 1890 and the sinking of the Lady Victoria Colliery begun on ground leased from the Marquis of Lothian—the colliery was named after his wife. When it was opened in 1895 it was a showpiece of Scottish colliery engineering and incorporated many innovations in its development and operation.

The pit was sunk adjacent to Lingerwood Colliery and connected underground to it. This was an essential feature of the design because, after an accident in Northumberland, in 1862, when over 200 men were trapped by a collapsed shaft, all collieries in Britain had to have two ways in and out. The ventilation fan for the two pits was sited at Lingerwood and the air circulated through their combined underground workings.

Lady Victoria maintained a consistently high output from six principal seams. It was closed in 1981, but now has a new role as the Scottish Mining Museum.

Lady Victoria's last coal

a Victorian Colliery

headgear & winding engine

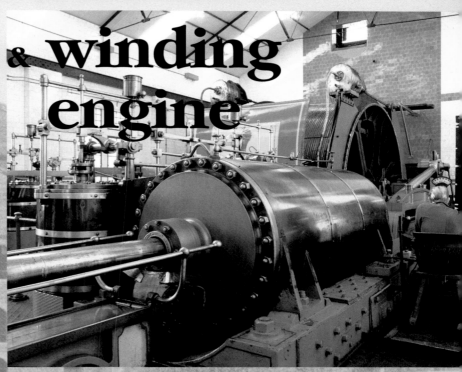

The operational capacity of a colliery was, to some extent, determined by the size of the shaft, headgear, winding engine and cages. The bigger they were the more coal could be brought to the surface. And at Lady Victoria they were big!

The eighty-five foot high headframe was built in 1893 by Sir William Arrol & Company of Glasgow—famous as the engineering firm that built the Forth Bridge. It was originally fitted with distinctive nineteen foot diameter, broad-spoked winding wheels—or whorls as they were often known in Scotland. These were supplied by Grant Ritchie & Company of Kilmarnock who also built the great winding engine which could lift over eleven tonnes and was one of the most powerful to be installed in Scotland. It was driven by steam and remained so up to the colliery's closure. The original winding drum—the engine had four drums during its working life—was twenty feet in diameter and ten feet, six inches wide and was driven by two horizontal forty-two inch cylinders with a seven foot stroke. The steel winding rope was wrapped around the drum and slung over the pulleys at the top of the headgear. When the drum was rotated one end of the rope was paid out while the other was wound in, so that one cage went down as the other came up. The cages acted as counterweights to each other.

The winding engineman sat on his high chair beside the right hand cylinder. His job was vitally important to the safety of miners and efficient operation of the colliery. Like all winding enginemen he had mechanical instruments to guide him and could not actually see the cages he was raising and lowering. As a result of a number of tragic accidents at other collieries, the system was fitted with an overwinder, a device which cutoff the steam, to prevent the cages from being moved too fast or being raised or lowered too far.

Lady Victoria Colliery was sunk on the eastern edge of the great Midlothian Coal Basin which underlies the valley of the Esk Rivers. It is about nine miles long and five and half miles wide and lies on a rough line running north east from Gorebridge and Penicuik. The coal basin dips steeply at the sides and levels out at its base, like a huge subterranean bath.

underground

There are over twenty separate seams of coal of a workable thickness in the basin, but not all of these could be mined, for reasons of economy, underground stability and quality. One of the seams the shaft passed through was a high quality industrial coal known as the Great Seam. It varied between six and eight feet thick and although it was worked in the early years, it was mainly extracted by the associated Lingerwood and Easthouses Collieries. Lady Victoria's workings were therefore concentrated on six main seams. Of these the four foot thick Splint and the three feet, nine inch Kailblades seams produced good steam coal—an essential commodity in the days when the right kind of coal was needed to raise steam in boilers. Household coal was produced from the two feet, nine inch Jewel seam and the three feet, two inch Coronation seam, but the best quality domestic coal came from the Diamond seam. It was only twenty inches thick and difficult to work, but it was superb. The Parrot or Cannel coal was also worked for a time for gas production.

The Newbattle Collieries, as the group of collieries in the Newtongrange area were called, operated in strata where the roof tended to be of shaly rock. The roof was prone to collapse, and so, in about 1912, the Lothian Coal Company developed a unique roof-support system using a timber prop inside a steel tube which allied the tensile strength of steel to the crushing strength of wood, much the same principle as that in reinforced concrete. The props were linked across the roof with corrugated steel straps, about six feet long. Although this system of roof support was initially expensive it offered long term economy because the props could be more easily recovered and reused. It also proved valuable during the First World War when there was a timber shortage and props were in short supply.

The main underground roadways were made to dimensions that were regarded at the time as generous: eight feet high and ten or twelve feet wide. The pit bottom was also larger than normal. But the company's foresight paid off, because as output increased, the bigger roads were able to handle more, large-capacity, tubs.

There was some stoop and room working of the Great Seam close to the shaft, but, apart from that, the colliery worked the longwall system throughout, with faces about 100 yards long. Electric coal cutters were used. Initially tubs were hand filled at the face and ponies used for haulage, but these were superseded by electrically driven conveyors.

Haulage engine

Loaded tubs at the pit bottom

coal face display

The museum's realistic coalface display features the more-modern system of coal cutting with a double ended shearer, armoured flexible conveyor and hydraulically operated roof supports.

Coal face exhibit with double-ended shearer

Roadway exhibit

The headgear rising through the tub circuit

At the time it was sunk the shaft was the deepest in Scotland, going down to a working depth of 1,624 feet. Most shafts at the time were rectangular and lined with timber, but Lady Victoria's was circular, twenty feet in diameter and lined with brick. It was also the first in Scotland to be walled at the same time as it was being sunk. This was done using a 'Galloway Scaffold' a platform with two decks which allowed the pit sinkers to work in safety while the bricklayers worked above them. Sinking was not without its problems because, at a depth of about 600 feet, water started to pour into the shaft at a rate of about 100 gallons a minute, and 180 feet lower another water 'feeder' of about 200 gallons a minute was cut. More water was encountered at over 1700 feet deep and the shaft back-filled to its finished depth.

Tub axle lubricator

Operator, loading and unloading tubs by hydraulic ram

Tubs and tipplers

shaft & tub circuit

The generous dimensions of the shaft allowed it to be equipped with large, double-decked cages. These required two landing stages at top and bottom of the shaft. In the colliery's early years the great winding engine could lift twelve loaded hutches, six on each deck of the cage, or forty-eight men. Later, when the tubs were increased in size, the cages held eight of them, four on each deck.

On the surface, as first designed, empty tubs were pushed onto the cage from one side and loaded ones taken off on the other. The full tubs were moved around a small-scale railway system known as the tub circuit. The tubs on the upper deck ran by gravity round a curve to the weighbridge and those on the lower deck were raised by a creeper chain to join them. This system was changed in 1962 to only one decking level, with the cages stopped and unloaded twice on the one level. Pneumatic rams superseded manual loading and some of the curved rail system was replaced by turntables—this is the layout that can be seen at the colliery today. After weighing, the tubs were run to the tipplers—rotating cradles that turned the tubs upside down to unload them.

Conveyors then fed the coal over jigging or shaker screens—vibrating metal plates, like giant sieves, which allowed the dross coal to fall through and be taken from under the screens, by scraper conveyor, to the washer. The larger lumps stayed on the conveyors which took them to the picking tables. These moved like conveyor belts, and men and boys stood beside them to pick pieces of stone out from amongst the coal as it passed in front of them. Women did this work at many collieries. Sodium lighting was installed over the picking tables in 1955. It made the coal glisten so that it was easier to distinguish from stone. After 'picking' the coal was delivered to the waiting railway wagons.

At the picking tables

Originally none of the coal produced at the colliery was washed, but around 1910 a washery was built to separate the small cannel coal from dirt. The fine coal was taken by scraper conveyor from the jigging screens to a storage pit and from there raised sixty feet by a bucket elevator to the washery. It was again passed over jigging screens, to separate it into five sizes, and directed to the appropriate wash tank. The three larger sizes were washed in bash or plunger tanks. These worked by forcing water back

washing the coal

and forth through a sieve mounted in the tank— the coal floated to the surface and the dirt fell through the sieve. The two smaller sizes of coal, known as peas and duff, were washed in tanks over a mineral known as feldspar which also acted as a sieve when the water was agitated and the tiny pieces of coal floated to the surface. The washer had a capacity of 100 tons an hour and used 1,000 gallons of water a minute, the water being reused after settling in tanks.

Conveyor from tippler to picking tables

Washer in the 1920s

Dense medium plant, with vertically rotating paddles

Dirty water from the bash tanks and feldspar beds of the old washer was allowed to settle in ponds adjacent to the original boiler house. Sediment was lifted out of these reservoirs by the dredger, a mechanism which consisted of a continuous chain of perforated buckets. Water drained through the perforations leaving very fine coal or 'duff' which was fed directly to the colliery's boilers.

The gas industry had stopped using cannel coal by the 1960s, and the washer was treating small coals for use in the Borders woollen mills and Portobello Power Station. When the new power station at Cockenzie came on-stream in 1968 it took much of the pit's output, but did not want treated coal and so the washeries were de-commissioned. Much of the old washer still exists and is believed to be the only surviving example of bash tanks and feldspar beds in Europe. The machinery is housed in the tallest building on the colliery site. Alongside is

an extension building which housed a re-washery. It was installed before 1932 to recover more small particles of coal, but has not survived.

A plant known as the Dense Medium Plant was constructed in 1963–4 to wash coal measuring over two inches. It had two units, one for Lady Victoria coal and one for coal from the associated collieries of Easthouses and Lingerwood. Each unit could treat 120 tons an hour. The 'dense medium' was a mineral imported from Sweden known as magnetite. It was suspended in water which was agitated by vertically rotating paddles. This separated dirt from the coal which floated to the surface, while the dirt sank. The cone-shaped tank adjacent to the plant was used to recover the magnetite. Dirty water from the Dense Medium Plant went to the Fines Treatment Plant to be cleansed and fed back into, what was in effect a closed circuit, so that polluted water was not discharged into natural water courses.

Washer discharging into railway wagons

Battery of twelve boilers, late 1920s

heat & power

Victorian collieries used steam power for much of their heavy equipment like winding and haulage engines, and pumps. Some of the coal produced by the colliery therefore went to fire its own boilers, to generate the steam that was used to win more coal—it was a circular process!

The original boiler house at Lady Victoria was equipped with six boilers. They were fitted with superheaters and operated at 100 pounds per square inch. Only five were in use at any one time, allowing one to be kept in reserve for cleaning and maintenance. A new boiler house was brought into use in 1924, equipped with a battery of twelve Lancashire boilers made by Tinkler, Shenton & Company of Manchester and purchased as old war stock from the munitions factory at Gretna. They operated at a pressure of 160 pounds per square inch and, as with the original boilers, two were kept in reserve at any one time. Economisers raised the water temperature before it entered the boilers. Towards the end of the colliery's life the number of boilers was reduced to eight, but Lady Victoria's management resisted converting the great winding engine to electricity and it continued to be steam-powered until closure.

Scottish collieries began using electricity in the late nineteenth century and were quicker to adapt to the use of electrically powered equipment than other parts of Britain. To begin with public electricity supplies were unable to deal with the load required by some collieries so they generated their own power for coal cutters, conveyors, pumps, lighting and a variety of other uses. Lady Victoria was originally equipped with two 1,000 kilowatt turbines which were driven by exhaust steam from the winding engine, or when this was not available by 'live' steam from the boilers. There were also backup turbines in case of breakdowns.

A new power station was built in 1924 to serve the three Newbattle pits—Lady Victoria, Lingerwood and Easthouses. The plant consisted of a single 5,000 kilowatt alternator, with four 1,000 kilowatt turbines in reserve. When the equipment reached the end of its useful life the collieries took their power from the now adequate National Grid. These power station buildings still exist. The old one is used for exhibitions and functions while visitors to the colliery enter by the new power station which also houses the museum shop and restaurant.

Workshops, late 1920s

workshops

All collieries needed access to workshops for the maintenance and manufacture of equipment. Often these were small operations, but at Lady Victoria a large workshop was set up for all the Newbattle Collieries. It was capable of looking after all the major plant including railway locomotives and employed engineers, blacksmiths, wagon smiths, joiners and electricians. A central workshop for the whole of the Lothian Area was established on the site by the National Coal Board in 1957.

laboratory

The laboratory at Lady Victoria was opened in 1921, one of a number set up around that time by an industry that was becoming increasingly aware of the need to know about the conditions men were working in. Coal, dust, water, air and colliery by-products were analysed there. The laboratory also examined oil and greases and the operations of the washery.

First aid practice

baths & medical centre

Many collieries were equipped with pit-head baths after the Miners' Welfare Fund was extended to provide funds for them, but Lady Victoria was not one of them. Indeed there was local opposition to the provision of pit-head baths, which appears to have stemmed from a desire amongst the women of the village to have baths put into their houses first! Pit-head baths were eventually opened by the NCB in 1954, their site across the main road made them convenient for both Lady Victoria and Lingerwood Collieries. A heated walkway led from the baths to Lady Victoria, and although the baths have been demolished, part of the walkway still spans the road.

The baths building was equipped with a canteen and bicycle sheds. The building also housed one of the largest medical centres at a Scottish colliery. It was staffed by a full-time nurse, assisted by qualified first-aiders and served all the collieries in the vicinity.